Jump, Frog

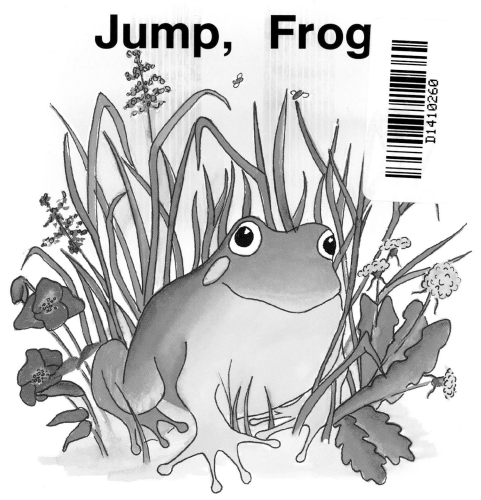

Story by Josie Stewart and Lynn Salem
Illustrations by Tori Mackie

A frog can jump.

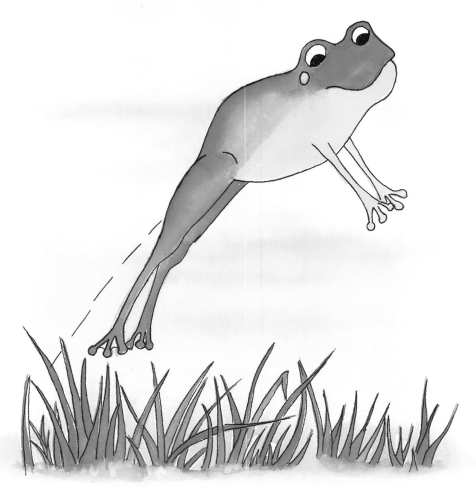

A frog can jump to a rock.

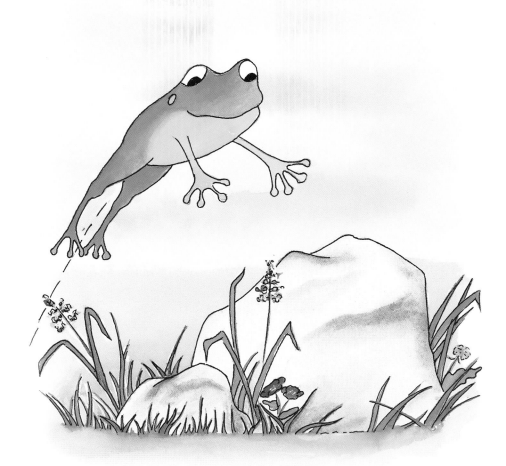

A frog can jump to Mom.

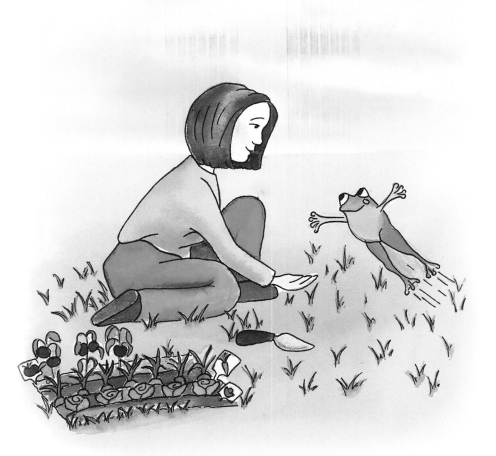

A frog can jump to a flower.

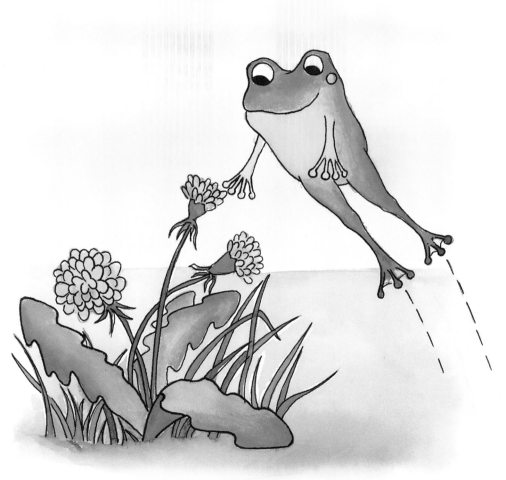

Jump, frogs, jump!

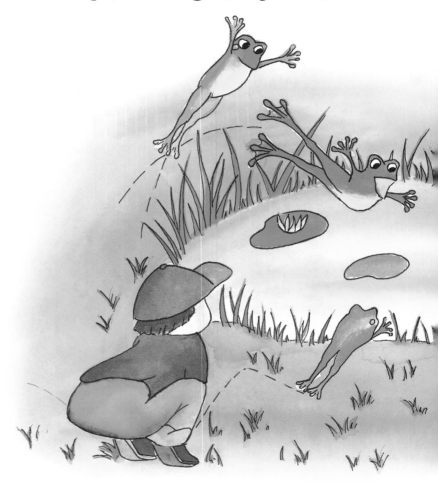

Jump, jump, jump!

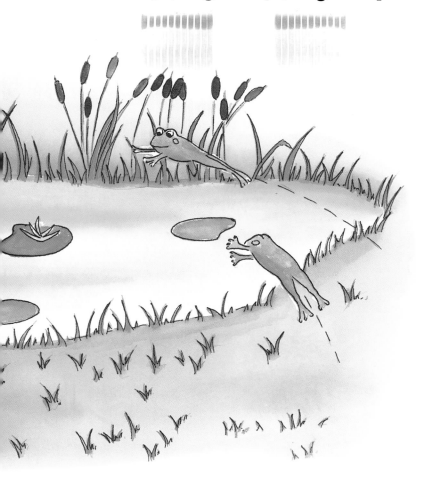

Frogs can jump.

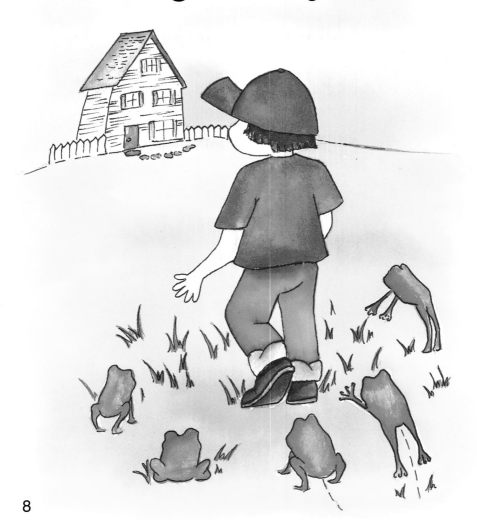